THIS
WORLD BOOK DAY
2020 BOOK
IS A GIFT FROM YOUR
LOCAL BOOKSELLER,
MATTHEW SYED AND
WREN & ROOK

#SHAREASTORY

CELEBRATE STORIES. LOVE READING.

My AWESOME Guide to GETTING GOOD AT STUFF

Matthew Syed

Illustrated by **TOBY TRIUMPH**

With **OLLIE MANN & LINDSEY SAGAR**

wren
&rook

First published in Great Britain in 2020 by Wren & Rook

Text copyright © Matthew Syed, 2020
Illustration copyright © Toby Triumph, 2018 & Hodder & Stoughton Limited, 2018 & 2020
Design copyright © Hodder & Stoughton Limited, 2020
All rights reserved.

The right of Matthew Syed and Toby Triumph, Ollie Mann & Lindsay Sagar to be identified
as the author and illustrators respectively of this Work has been asserted by them in
accordance with the Copyright, Designs & Patents Act 1988.

ISBN: 978 1 5263 6268 1 | Export edition ISBN: 978 1 5263 6280 3
10 9 8 7 6 5 4 3 2 1

MIX
Paper from
responsible sources
FSC® C104740
www.fsc.org

Wren & Rook
An imprint of
Hachette Children's Group
Part of Hodder & Stoughton
Carmelite House
50 Victoria Embankment
London EC4Y 0DZ

An Hachette UK Company
www.hachette.co.uk | www.hachettechildrens.co.uk

Publishing Director: Debbie Foy | Managing Editor: Liza Miller
Art Director: Laura Hambleton | Designed by Thy Bui

Printed in the UK

CONTENTS

INTRODUCTION

My mum has had to send out a search party to find me
not once, but **TWICE** in my life. The second time was
after a mix-up on a bus to Norway from my house in
Reading (you might have read about this in my book *You
Are Awesome*, but if you haven't, don't worry). The short
version is that I got on the bus to the wrong Bergen and
ended up lost in a motorway lay-by in northern Germany
rather than arriving at the Norwegian town called Bergen
where I was supposed to be training for table tennis. That
time, my mum was more worried than she was furious.
After all, she had bought the bus ticket in the first place –
to the wrong Bergen. So surely she had to shoulder some
of the blame for that one?

But the first time it happened ... she was mad. So angry,
in fact, that I thought she might explode. Even angrier
than when my brother landed a magnet on my head
during an ill-advised experiment to see if it would stick
to our bedroom ceiling. It didn't. And my head was
bleeding for nearly a week.

But where were we? Oh yes. A search party. Yes, the
police had been called to look for me.

6

I had left the house with my brother at 4 p.m.. By 9 p.m., we still weren't back. Understandably, my mum was pretty concerned. In truth, there was no need for any search party. We were less than 200 metres from the house. But we didn't know that. She could have shouted to us and we would have heard. But she didn't know that.

We were just doing The Network. My mum had no idea about The Network. (Let's try and keep it that way. Thankfully I don't think she is eligible for a World Book Day voucher, so I doubt she'll be reading this.)

I lived in a town called Reading. On a very normal street with lots of other very similar houses, with similar gardens, surrounded by lots of very similar roads with more similar houses and gardens. You might say it was a 'network' of very ordinary living arrangements. Do you see where I'm going with this? Anyway, most of the kids on my street were brilliant at table tennis. That was no accident. We had the best club and the best coach at the end of the road, and we played **ALL THE TIME**. But sometimes after playing table tennis, we would decide to do The Network on the way home.

The Network was a kind of game. We invented it by accident when we discovered a whole series of overgrown paths weaving between and behind the houses in our neighbourhood. We (literally) tripped over it when we tried to take a shortcut home one day and ducked behind a garage at the top of the street to see what was there. To our amazement, we found an old path that didn't look like it had been used for years. It was overrun with wiry bushes but it had a small opening just wide enough to jam ourselves through. And that is how we discovered The Network, a very thorny maze of passageways running behind all the back gardens. We realised that you could go into it at one end and (after crawling under branches and swerving a few wasp nests) pop out on the other side of the block of roads. The whole idea of The Network was to enter it on one street and race each other to get to one of the other exits on a totally different street. The potential to get lost was high. So whenever we did The Network, one of three things usually happened:

1 We got shouted at by Mr Dixon, who lived next to the only entry point to The Network that went down the side of a house rather than a garage. He used to put his rubbish bin at what he thought was the end of a short path next to his house. But it was actually an entrance to The Network, and we always knocked his bin over as we scrambled through the bushes. It was a metal one and it made a noise like a steel band when it crashed to the ground. Mr Dixon didn't appear to enjoy this particular steel band. It made him shout. A lot.

2 We managed to navigate our way to

THE GREAT
((FRISBEE COLLECTOR

(a.k.a. a huge tree in my back garden). The GFC was high and impossible to climb, and over the years we had thrown countless tennis balls, footballs and frisbees into its top branches, where they remained for evermore. It looked like a badly decorated Christmas tree and the baubles could have stocked a whole sports shop. You could see it for miles. Right by the GFC, The Network forked in two, with one path coming out at the side of our garage – a fail-safe route home.

3 We ended up entangled somewhere we didn't recognise at all. Then a wrong turn would happen.

And another. By then we'd be totally lost. And although this was all going on in the undergrowth hidden within the block where we all lived, it was always a shock to pop out somewhere totally unexpected.

Number 3 happened the night the search party was called. On this particular evening, we left the table-tennis club at 5.30 p.m. to get home for dinner. (We were excited about dinner because my mum had promised to try out a new shape of pasta, the one with the bows. And we were starving.) But we decided to do The Network on the way home. The thing is, it was winter, so it was really dark and cold. And we'd never done The Network in the dark. It turns out there was a good reason for that.

We couldn't see the frisbee tree. Someone, somewhere took a wrong turn and we all followed. And suddenly, after quite a few scratches from some unforeseen rose bushes, we popped out. But we didn't recognise where we were. There were no mobile phones with maps back then, so we were well and truly lost. Although we weren't really. We were still on the block, 200 m from our house. And if we'd looked at the street signs, we would have known that and walked home in two minutes flat. But we didn't. We carried on in The Network, getting more and more lost.

In the end, we were in The Network for about two hours. When we heard the police sirens, we popped out to the street to see what the commotion was about. Only then did we realise we were back on Avalon Road and less than 30 seconds from home.

My brother and I ran back and tried to walk in casually through the front door as if nothing was amiss. That failed. We were covered in mud and my brother had managed (don't ask me how) to get a worm in his hair. And that's when my mum went

B.A.N.A.N.A.S.

So what on earth has this got to do with getting good at stuff? Well, if you happen to have read *You Are Awesome*, you'll know the story about how so many people on my street in Reading got to be brilliant table-tennis players. But if you haven't read it yet, let's have a quick recap. The most important bit is that it wasn't by chance that the England table-tennis team

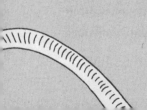

mainly consisted of kids from my road. It happened because we all wanted to practise, had the opportunity to practise and all did the practice. We had a great coach and a table-tennis club at the end of the road. So my street wasn't blessed by some freak alien who was making everyone good at table tennis. We were doing it ourselves. With our dedication and a bit of luck.

I'm letting you know about The Network because it tells us something similar. My brother and I talked about it for hours once my mum had stopped yelling. (We had hours to kill. We were sent to our room for the whole weekend.)

Navigating The Network had been impossible at first. A small wrong turning could take us on a totally different path to the one we expected. We had to deal with the unfamiliar terrain and find our way back from a different place. But over time, we got really good at The Network. In my next life I want to come back as a racehorse because I am absolutely brilliant at jumping over hedges and bushes. If we meet, ask me to show you. I honestly think I could win the Grand National. But The Network taught me some more important stuff too:

- When you do something often, even if it is hard at first – especially if it is hard – the progress you can make is staggering. You can end up being far better than you might ever have imagined.

- Your ability to see patterns and find a route to your destination or goal gets easier every time you do something. In fact, the wiring in your brain actually **CHANGES** as you do things that are difficult, so that next time you'll find it easier.

- Things often don't go quite as you imagined. **DON'T PANIC.** If you've done the hard work and tried your best, you'll learn from any mistakes and be stronger next time. Don't give up. If we had, we'd still be somewhere in an alleyway off Moor Copse Close.

- And try not to get a worm in your hair. Ever. The slime is impossible to get rid of.

Now, maybe you only picked this book up because it was free, and you decided that if it isn't that good, you can always use it to wedge your bedroom door shut. Or maybe, just maybe, you are a tiny bit curious about getting good at stuff.

So stick with me and let's get on with it. I'm going to let you in on some more secrets to success. Read on ...

1

Do you want the good news or the bad news first?
I never understand why anyone ever wants the good
news first. No matter how good the good news is, you
know that you've only got a big downer coming.

So, let's start with the bad news: getting good at stuff is
Not Easy. It's hard. It takes time. And effort.

That's the downer. You're coping with it okay I think,
but now you are definitely ready for a mood lifter. And
the good news is … **ANYONE** can get waaaay better
at (almost) anything. Now that is mega news, right?
Life-changing news. But it can still be difficult to know
where to start. Taking the first step can sometimes
seem impossible.

But maybe it wouldn't feel so impossible if we knew a
little bit more about how people actually get good at
stuff. There's a lot of 'fake news' out there, i.e. an awful
lot of myths about how the super-successful made it
to the top. And the even bigger issue is that sometimes

people don't want you to know the truth. They don't necessarily want you to know about all the mistakes they made on the way up. They want to keep all of their hard work a secret. Sometimes, they want you to believe the myth that they are just naturally brilliant and have been **INCREDIBLE** at what they do since the moment they were born.

So let's blow this fake news thing wide open: let's look at these myths, bust them and uncover exactly what it does take to get (really) good at stuff.

MYTH 1: YOU'RE EITHER BORN WITH A TALENT OR YOU'RE NOT.

This is my least-favourite myth. Actually, it isn't. Not of all time. My least-favourite is the one about how **BEING** cold makes you catch an actual cold. Don't get me started on that. Colds are caused by viruses. They are not caused by forgetting to put your coat on or getting your hair wet in the rain. That's **FAKE NEWS**.

But this myth about talent is definitely near the bottom of my list. And I find it particularly annoying because so many people seem to believe it! One look at Taylor Swift and they assume she must have been born with a microphone in her hand. A glance at Lionel Messi and they think that if you sequenced his DNA it would have an actual football in the helix. And this myth creates a problem. If you believe that you need to be born with a gift, then it can really limit your willingness to try to get good at stuff. Why would you bother? If your destiny was decided at birth, what would be the point in working hard to improve?

BUT IT IS A MYTH. IT'S FAKE NEWS.

Here is the real secret. If you look at the life story of almost any super-successful person, you'll see that their success was a journey over many years. It involved them taking a risk, getting started and working incredibly hard to achieve their goal. And **THAT** is a method we could all at least try – to work hard and get good at something. I did, with table tennis. I wasn't born with the bat in my hand able to do a smash kill (that's a table tennis shot, in case you were wondering...), but I eventually made it to the Olympics.

I also find it amazing that everyone is so quick to discount the unbelievable things they have already mastered. And then somehow jump to the conclusion that they'll never master the things they are not already fantastic at.

Let me prove it to you. You are already brilliant. At loads of things. Stuff that you've actually worked really hard to achieve, but I bet you give yourself no credit for whatsoever.

Talking is one of them. No, honestly, talking is tricky! Whatever your first language is, you didn't come hurtling into this world able to ask for extra jam on your toast, able to discuss the merits of different types of emojis or able to shout at your brother when he thought it would be funny to swap one of your table-tennis balls for a boiled egg. (They're not even the same shape!)

But here's the thing. No one is born with the ability to understand English or French or Cantonese. But after just 12 months, the average one-year-old has learnt to recognise 50 words. The average six-year-old can understand **10,000** and, by age 12, their vocabulary has increased to a whopping **50,000** words! This is no accident. You have practised this skill, worked on it. Listened closely to those talking around you, committing words to memory. With practice, you've developed an ability to order the words into sentences. And hey presto, you are headlining your family's annual Christmas joke-telling competition (or maybe not, but you get my point...).

It's true that some of us will recognise a few more words than others. But almost all of us can talk effectively. Communicate. And be understood.

This isn't easy. And yet we give ourselves no credit for it. Despite the fact that we can obviously get very good at things, we jump to the conclusion that we'll never be any good at maths, or have the co-ordination for tennis, or get the part in the school play.

I'll give you another example. We are brilliant at recognising patterns. Literally amazing. And this takes practice. Have a look at the pictures below. What do you see?

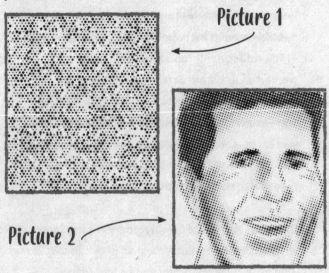

Picture 1

Picture 2

Both are black dots arranged on a white background. And, to a newborn baby or an alien from outer space, both pictures would look almost the same. Just dots. Random dots.

But I'm guessing that you think **Picture 2** looks like someone? Even more specifically, a man. Who isn't really old, or a child. Who is smiling.

You probably don't think it, but

★ THIS IS AN ★
INCREDIBLE SKILL.

It is no accident that you can recognise this pattern in a random collection of blobs. This is a skill you have spent years honing. You are amazing at this.

An alien who had never seen a human face before would have no chance at spotting the pattern. But you have spent hours studying the tiny differences in the faces of those around you. Spotting emotions on people's faces, and the small differences that reveal someone's age. And after all this practice, you are awesome at it. How often do you mistake David Walliams for Simon Cowell? Never. Yet they are both men of a similarish age, with white skin, dark hair, two eyes and one nose. But you would never get them mixed up. Ever.

So are you high-fiving yourself yet? Are you presenting a medal to yourself on a makeshift Olympic podium? (Or am I the only one who made one of those?) I doubt you are.

Instead, I bet you are taking for granted this amazing skill you have worked so hard on, and meanwhile you are probably worrying about why you haven't yet nailed your science homework or the skateboard trick you've been grappling with.

INTERESTING FACT:
INUIT PEOPLE CAN SEE MANY MORE SHADES OF WHITE THAN WE CAN.

Why? Because they have got some kind of special eyesight that the rest of us weren't born with?
NO – because they have spent more time in the Arctic than we have and so have developed their skills at identifying different types of snow.

Now, here is the problem. At some point, we start to believe that it is okay to limit ourselves and the potential we have to get good at stuff. We start to believe in the myth.

THE FAKE NEWS
THAT YOU'RE EITHER BORN WITH A TALENT OR YOU'RE NOT.

Most people are lucky enough to be able to walk and talk. And that's because you don't see babies thinking, 'This walking business is hard. I've fallen over twice today already. You know what, I don't think I am cut out for walking. I'll give it a miss.'

Or, 'Talking is tricky. I've got to try and learn thousands of these word things. It's all a bit too much effort. I'm not bothered if I can't talk anyway. I'll save the energy.'

No! Babies get on with it. They give it a go. If they make a mistake, they keep on trying until they master it.

So don't believe the myth. You are already an awesome learning machine. I promise. I've proved it. So apply the same principles to whatever it might be that you'd like to get good at

and go for it.

MYTH 2: MISTAKES = DISASTER

This is my third-least favourite myth. After the one about colds and the one about talent. If this one was true then my life would be a catalogue of major disasters. Because there have been a lot of big mistakes. Made by me.

You already know at least one of them. First, there was the time I got the bus to the wrong Bergen, a big error. Then there was the time I lost in my first match at the Sydney Olympics. To Peter Franz, a guy I'd beaten loads of times before. I'd spent four years of my life training for that moment, but I got too nervous. That was a mistake.

And then there might be some mistakes you don't know about. The time I bowled a cricket ball at full pelt at my brother, who was waiting bat in hand at the end of the garden. We assumed he would hit it perfectly and either I'd catch it or it would land in the GFC. It didn't. Instead, it ricocheted off the washing line and smashed straight through next door's _____ That was **DEFINITELY**

Or there was the time I lost 40 table-tennis matches in a row on the Japanese Super Circuit. They were 40 bad days, I can tell you. You only earned money if you won, so I was broke. On day 41, when I had my first win, I went out and spent most of my winnings on the equivalent of a Pot Noodle to celebrate.

But it is from these mistakes that we learn things. You see, the only way you can get good at stuff is if you know where your gaps are, what your weak spots are, what you need to work on. Mistakes are brilliant for that. They tell you exactly what you don't know. Which is what you **NEED** to know.

Wrong answers in a test? Awesome! Those are showing you the stuff you don't know. Let's work on that, then. No point in working on the stuff you can already do. That is a waste of time. And we're busy people.

Missed a few catches in your netball or cricket match? Fantastic! That'll be the skill to focus on. Get your brother to start throwing balls at you and make sure (unlike me) you catch it before it dents your head. You'll soon be nailing it on the sports field.

Fluffed your lines in rehearsal? Brilliant! Now you know exactly which ones to practise to be word-perfect at the next run-through.

The idea that you should be embarrassed about making a mistake is one of the biggest myths out there. And super-successful people know this. They've all spent years learning from the mistakes they've made and using the information these mistakes have given them to perfect their skills.

Sometimes you make these mistakes when it isn't a practice. You might make them in a real exam. Or in a real match. I did. I lost in front of eight million people watching the Olympics on the BBC. (I know what you're thinking. Eight million can't have been watching table tennis. I wonder about that myself. Maybe the 100 metres was up just after my match?) But I learnt from that mistake too. I learnt one of my most valuable lessons of all. That life doesn't stop or end if you make a mistake like that.

There is always another chance. Another path to follow. There wasn't another Olympics for me (I was too old), but there were other great matches I won after that, and guess what? I had learnt to manage my nerves a little bit better. And there were other things I could try to be good at too. After the Sydney Olympics, I decided to have a go at writing (I'll let you be the judge of whether that choice was a mistake ...).

Did you know that J.K. Rowling had her first Harry Potter book rejected 12 times before a publisher finally took a chance on her?

You heard it right – 12 times she had to pick herself up off the floor and decide to try again. It must have been pretty discouraging, talking to friends and having to tell them that she still hadn't got anyone to believe in her boy wizard. But luckily for us, Rowling didn't give up and she didn't let the failures get to her – she just doubled down and tried, tried, tried again. We never would have discovered the 12 uses of dragons' blood if she'd given up after receiving 12 rejections.

MYTH 3: EVERYONE IS MUCH BETTER THAN ME. I'LL NEVER CATCH UP.

Okay, let's start with a brilliant quote to tackle this one:

'IT IS NOT ALWAYS THE PEOPLE THAT START OUT THE SMARTEST, WHO END UP THE SMARTEST.'

CAROL DWECK, AWESOME PROFESSOR OF PYSCHOLOGY AT STANFORD UNIVERSITY

○ It seems like an impossible dream that **YOU**, usually always picked last in PE, could ever join the football team.

○ You want to fall over laughing at the thought of auditioning for the school play when at the moment you're too nervous to even put your hand up in class.

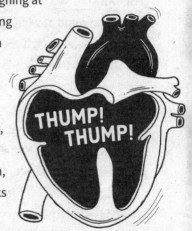

THUMP!
THUMP!

○ You don't have a chance, having never really got the hang of long division, of getting near-top marks in a maths test.

But you might. You really might. Because we've demonstrated that you are an awesome learning machine, capable of amazing things – if you make the effort.

THE BAD NEWS: You might put in the hard work and never make it to the Olympic podium (I didn't). You might not become prime minister (I haven't done that – yet). Or win a Nobel Prize (I certainly haven't done that – and it's looking quite unlikely. I haven't really worked on my physics or economics lately. And I haven't had the time to try negotiating international peace either).

THE GOOD NEWS: It doesn't matter if you are not the best in the world at what you decide you want to be. What we know is that if you get out there, give it a go and try your hardest, you'll be a whole lot better than when you started. It's almost certain you'll have a lot of fun along the way. And you never know, you **MIGHT** end up being the best in the world. But one thing we can be totally sure of is that if you don't ever start, take a risk and dare to fail, you **DEFINITELY** won't be.

So it doesn't matter when you begin. It doesn't matter if others are already better than you. We have no idea what we are capable of until we get out there, start putting in the effort and begin learning from our mistakes along the way.

In the words of the amazing author George Eliot (look her up),

'IT'S NEVER TOO LATE TO BE WHAT YOU MIGHT HAVE BEEN.'

Here's a list of people who didn't achieve great things until they were 35 or older. (I know, difficult to comprehend being this old. But it goes to show that you should **NEVER STOP LEARNING**.)

- Samuel L. Jackson getting his big Hollywood break
- Charles Darwin publishing *On the Origin of Species*
- Ray Kroc founding McDonald's
- J.K. Rowling publishing *Harry Potter and the Philosopher's Stone*

FAILURE TAUGHT ME THINGS ABOUT MYSELF THAT I COULD HAVE LEARNED NO OTHER WAY.

J.K. ROWLING, AWESOME AUTHOR
AND FAN OF FAILURE

So if you want to get really good at stuff, here are my three top tips:

1 Dream **BIG**!

2 Don't be afraid to fail. This is an easy thing to say and less easy to do. But believe me when I say that failure is inevitable on the road to success.

3 Hard work pays off. So roll up your sleeves and get practising. Hard.

LET'S DO THIS.

2

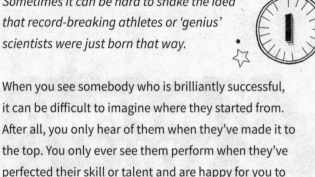

Sometimes it can be hard to shake the idea that record-breaking athletes or 'genius' scientists were just born that way.

When you see somebody who is brilliantly successful, it can be difficult to imagine where they started from. After all, you only hear of them when they've made it to the top. You only ever see them perform when they've perfected their skill or talent and are happy for you to watch. So it can be **IMPOSSIBLE** to imagine all of the work they have put in and all of the mistakes they will certainly have made on their long journey.

Here are some stories about a few of my own personal heroes. Today, their success seems kind of inevitable. 'Of course Bill Gates founded the world's most successful computer company – he's a tech wizard!' But did you know that Bill didn't even touch a computer until secondary school? And Beyoncé may seem like she's a natural performer – so incredible to watch on stage that you could never hope to be as good as she is – but that's because you don't see all the hours of practice she puts in behind the scenes.

So if these guys can do it,

WHY CAN'T YOU?

AWESOME ACHIEVERS

BEYONCÉ

In 2018, Beyoncé set the Coachella festival stage alight. Reviews around the world gushed about her headlining performance – one newspaper said she was 'a solo star of unconquerable talent'. Crikey, it sounds like she's never made a mistake in her life. But far from it. Beyoncé started to perform at a very young age, entering school talent competitions when she was just seven. At the age of eight, Beyoncé was part of a group called Girl's Tyme. They entered a TV talent competition but didn't win. Beyoncé says their mistake was choosing a rubbish song.

But the true secret to Bey's success is not some mythical talent she was born with, it's that she works really, really hard. **THAT'S** why she crushes it.

When you look beneath the glitz, Beyoncé spent a whole year planning that Coachella performance, making sure it was the show of a lifetime. Once all the plans were in place, it was time to get practising. She and her team of dancers did 11-hour rehearsals for weeks to guarantee that every step was in sync. So when she took to the stage and her flawless vocals and dancing set the stage alight, her perfection seemed effortless – though it was anything but.

'AS SOON AS I ACCOMPLISH ONE THING, I JUST SET A HIGHER GOAL. THAT'S HOW I'VE GOTTEN TO WHERE I AM.'

BEYONCÉ, SLAYER OF SONG AND DANCE PRACTICE AND ALL-ROUND AWESOME ACHIEVER.

ELLIE SIMMONDS

When Ellie was 13, she won two Paralympic gold medals
for Great Britain in freestyle swimming, despite being
the youngest person on the team. She's been to two
more Paralympic Games since, and has bagged a total
of five gold medals. But guess what? Ellie wasn't born
wearing swimming goggles – she became a champion
because she loved to be in the water and was
DETERMINED to win!

Ellie has achondroplasia, or dwarfism. When she was
five, her parents took her to a pool for the first time
– and she loved it. Her favourite thing was to zoom
through the water as fast as she could. Training was
tough though, because her parents didn't make any
special allowances for her disability. She practised
hard, entering races against able-bodied swimmers

and winning a lot of the time. When she started formally competing in events for disabled swimmers, all that tough practice paid off – she became one of the fastest in the world.

Ellie is back in training now, aiming to compete in her fourth Paralympic Games in Tokyo in 2020. I can't wait to see how she gets on, but one thing's for sure – win or lose, she will have given it her all.

BILL GATES

Today, Bill Gates is famous for being the man that gave the world Microsoft – a company he started when he was only 20 years old. When you picture him as a kid, you probably imagine he was brilliant at computers and tech from as soon as he could toddle, right? But that's **NOT TRUE** at all – when Bill Gates was 10 years old, he was bored at school, struggling with dyslexia and grumpy at home. And believe it or not, he'd never clapped eyes on a real computer – they were still pretty new when he was young in the 1960s. Thankfully for the rest of the world, he moved schools – and that new school was one of the first in the United States to get a computer.

At first, he didn't really know what he was doing. But he fell in love with the computer and spent his lunchtimes learning programming languages with his friends. He practised more and more and got better and better. By the time he was 16, he started his first company, Traf-o-Data. You might think that that's it – by the time he was a teenager, Bill was an entrepreneur making stacks of money and never stopped. But actually, Traf-o-Data was an **EPIC** fail.

Traf-o-Data built devices that counted the number of cars on the road, and at just 16, Bill was pitching the product to the traffic manager of the city of Seattle. There was only one problem – the machine didn't work! The company never properly got off the ground, and soon after that it went bust.

That failure would have been enough to put many people off technology for life. But not Bill. He decided to learn from his mistakes and start a new business. Microsoft released their first product two years later, and the rest, as they say, is history!

Everyone has moments where they doubt
themselves from time to time – I definitely do.
So whenever I'm looking at a big goal I'm setting
myself and I feel like I'm not sure where to begin,
remembering these incredible stories and others
like them really helps me to get stuck in.

3

I think about that Bill Gates story a lot. Sometimes I wonder how I would spend 103 billion dollars if I had his money. Spending that would actually be a full-time job. It would be exhausting. Even if I took my time over it, say 50 years. That would still mean spending 5.5 million dollars every single day for 50 years. With no day off. Wow.

But mainly I think about the risk he took to set up his first company when he was pretty young, how he must have felt when it all crashed down around him, and then how he picked himself up and changed the world.

And Bill's (we're on first-name terms, right?) story is not unusual. Most people who have succeeded didn't do it on their first attempt.

(VERY) FAMOUS FAILURES

Scarily talented filmmaker **STEVEN SPIELBERG** was rejected by the University of Southern California's film school three times. But they awarded him an honorary degree in 1994 and he even became a trustee of the university in 1996!

Unbelievably, world-famous talk-show superstar **OPRAH WINFREY** was once fired by a TV producer because she was 'unfit for television'!

Expert fryer **COLONEL SANDERS'** Kentucky Fried Chicken recipe was rejected 1,009 times before he found a buyer!

Billionaire entrepreneur **JAMES DYSON** was no sucker (sorry…) even though he created a whopping 5,126 prototypes of his bagless vacuum cleaner before it was suitable to be sold in the shops.

Rapper **JAY-Z** couldn't get any record labels to sign him for years. Now he's one of the bestselling music artists of all time!

Hollywood actress **CAREY MULLIGAN** was rejected from every drama school she applied to!

Bright ideas man **THOMAS EDISON** invented 10,000 failed versions of the light bulb before he found one that really worked.

So, these stories are interesting, right?
They make me think three things:

1 Getting good at stuff really does take quite a lot of work, with lots of failures pretty likely to happen. You might not get it right first time.

2 How on earth did 1,009 people reject that chicken recipe? He can't have given them the family-sized bucket (that is the only explanation I can think of, anyway).

3 Imagine what would have happened if these guys had given up or, worse still, never dared to try in the first place.

Fear of failure does that. It can mean we don't even dare to start. Imagine if these guys had never even tried. Well, we'd be hoovering our bedrooms very badly in the dark, that's for sure. And we wouldn't be watching *Jurassic Park* while eating a Mighty Bucket For One either.

No matter what we decide we would like to be – plumber, musician, TV presenter, blogger, vlogger, doctor, politician, table-tennis player, artist, actress, computer hacker, scientist, environmental campaigner, data engineer, bed-warmer (yes, apparently this is a thing) – taking the first step might seem daunting. It might even be embarrassing to admit that you've got such a big dream.

But why? You don't have to make it to a Hollywood audition straight after you've decided to be an actor, or start neurosurgery straight after you've told your friend you want to be a doctor. And I bet those bed-warmers aren't heating up a super-kingsize at the Ritz Hotel on day one either. No way, they'll have worked their way up from a camp bed at the local B&B. To illustrate this, check out the following stories…

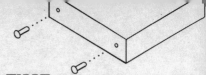

ONE STEP AT A TIME

In the 1940s, a small boy called Ingvar Kamprad was growing up in a small town in southern Sweden.

STEP 1: He discovered that he could buy boxes of matches in bulk in the Swedish capital of Stockholm at significantly cheaper prices than he could in his home town. So Ingvar would buy them up and sell each box to his neighbours for a good profit.

STEP 2: After a while, he began selling Christmas decorations, pencils, pens and seeds.

STEP 3: Finally, he added furniture to his offerings.

The end of the story: Ingvar opened IKEA, a fantastically successful superstore chain with shops around the world selling awesome meatballs, and some furniture too. And if you are interested, IK is his initials, E stands for Elmtaryd (the farm where Ingvar grew up), and A is for Agunnaryd (Ingvar's hometown).

On that basis, if I set up a mega-business it would have to be called MSER (Matthew Syed, Earley, Reading).

Not sure it has the same ring to it? Anyway, that is not the point. The point is that Ingvar didn't establish IKEA straight away. So take small steps first. Start by selling matches. Actually, **DEFINITELY** don't start by selling matches. It won't help you get into the school play and you'll probably get arrested. But you get what I mean.

Small steps can lead to

BIG THINGS.

There'll be mistakes and failures along the way, for sure. You've already heard about my mega-mistakes. Let me introduce you to somebody else ...

There was once a kid who didn't feel great about himself – in fact, he didn't like talking that much, and he was nine years old before he could really speak confidently out loud to another person. School was tough – one of his headteachers expelled him, and another told him he'd never amount to anything. Charming.

When he was a teenager, he decided that he'd try to be an electrical engineer. But he failed the exam. Then he thought he could be a teacher. He got decent enough grades at university, but none of his professors wanted to recommend him for a job teaching maths and physics.

It's not looking good, is it?

But here's the thing. You've probably heard of this guy. Because he went on to win a Nobel Prize in physics.

EVERYTHING *went*

PEAR
SHAPED

HIS NAME WAS
ALBERT EINSTEIN.

So, just like J.K. Rowling and Bill Gates, Albert Einstein stacked up some serious failures in his life. But I suspect that what he learnt from these early setbacks made him the brilliant mathematician and physicist that he became. Because this is exactly what science, technology, maths and physics are all about. You experiment, find out where your theory or your product doesn't work. You learn from it and make a new product or theory which is even better!

'IN THE MIDDLE OF DIFFICULTY LIES OPPORTUNITY.'

**ALBERT EINSTEIN,
MISTAKE-MAKER AND AND AWESOME MATHEMATICIAN**

SO
THESE
ARE MY
TOP
TIPS
FOR
TAKING A
LEAP

1 Taking the first step is the hardest one – but you won't make any progress without it. So ...

2 Be **BRAVE**! Take the first step!

3 **OWN** your failures, don't pretend they didn't happen. They'll show you what you don't know. And what you need to know if you're going to get good at stuff.

4 Then take the second step. And the third. And by that point, you are well on your way.

MISSION CONTROL
A.K.A. YOUR BRAIN!

4

*Have you ever stopped to think about how ridiculously jaw-droppingly, mind-blowingly **BRILLIANT** your brain is?*

I bet you haven't.

But I'm serious. Maybe you're just sitting there quietly reading this book. Pretty straightforward, right? You might assume that your brain is practically on standby. Like a TV, sitting there, doing nothing, waiting for someone to press a button. **NOPE**. Here are just some of the things that your brain is working away at ferociously right now, just so you can read these words on a page:

○ Controlling your breathing. Breathing in oxygen and breathing out carbon dioxide.
○ Blinking your eyelids regularly so your eyeballs don't dry out.

- Keeping your heart beating so you don't, you know, drop dead.
- Telling your stomach to keep digesting that cheese sandwich you had for lunch.
- Holding your head upright so you can look at the page.
- Converting those ink lines on the pages into a pattern of words that you recognise and can understand. (Reading is a skill that you have practised and become amazing at. Probably without even thinking about how complex it is.)
- Instructing your fingers to turn the page every once in a while.
- Keeping an ear out for your annoying little sister's stealthy footsteps in case she's about to direct a paper aeroplane straight at your head.

Phew. That's a lot of stuff going on. And you're not even breaking into a sweat! In fact, the human brain can juggle over 1,000 processes every single second.

So how does that compare to a computer? The world's fastest computer is called the Summit and was made by IBM in 2018. Here's a handy comparison between it and your awesome brain:

THE SUMMIT **VS** YOUR BRAIN

THE SUMMIT		YOUR BRAIN
$200 million	**COST**	Free (as far as I know, although your parents might disagree given all the biscuits you eat)
About the same as 6,000 homes would need	**POWER REQUIRED**	About the same as a small lightbulb needs
Two tennis courts	**SIZE**	Slightly smaller than your head
308,400 kg (more than an A380 aircraft)	**WEIGHT**	1.3 kg
1 billion billion per second	**CALCULATIONS PER SECOND**	Impossible to know – but it's estimated that it might also be 1 billion billion per second!
No	**CAN IT REWIRE ITSELF?**	Yes

61

Based on that comparison, it looks like we are winning hands down. Against even the biggest and best supercomputer. **AWESOME**.

((BAD NEWS))
ALERT! Computers can calculate things much, much faster than our brains can. This is because we have to remember the numbers, symbols and then the methods for the calculations. But computers are programmed with all the rules they need for super-speedy sums.

((GOOD NEWS))
ALERT! A computer can't do complex tasks that we find really easy. So if you asked a computer to fold some bedsheets, it would take ages. Plus our brains feel emotions, think about the future and can taste the flavour of apples.

Our brains really are **VERY AWESOME**. This is what we have on our side. Powering us. Literally getting us good at stuff.

'THE **MASSIVE** PROCESSOR KNOWN AS THE **HUMAN BRAIN** IS NEITHER A **LITERATURE ORGAN** OR A MATH ORGAN. IT IS BOTH AND MORE.'

JOHN GREEN, AUTHOR, WISE WORDSMITH
AND BRAIN BOOSTER

The reason your brain can do all of these amazing things is because it's like a fantastically complicated communications hub. A bit like NASA Mission Control – all of this information flows into it, and then your brain makes crucial decisions and fires out orders to all the other parts of your body, reacting to the information it's received.

The key to making this system work is our central nervous system, which is like a messaging network. Our nerves are information superhighways, delivering signals to and from the brain at incredible speed. Each of our nerve superhighways is made up of individual cells called neurons. We have **GAZILLIONS** of them. An almost incomprehensible amount. In fact, a piece of brain tissue the size of a grain of sand can contain 100,000 neurons.

But why on earth are we going through this brain anatomy lesson I can hear you asking?

Because our brain's ability to grow and make new neural connections is yet more proof that **MYTH 1** (the one about needing to be born with talent) is totally fake news.

The neural pathways in your brain aren't fixed. You are not born with a set number which may or may not be more than your brother has. No – you can build them. The harder you work and the more difficult your practice is, the more neural connections you make. And the longer you practise something for, the stronger those connections in your brain become – making the skills you are practising easier and easier.

This really is the most **MEGA** news. This is **THE SECRET** to getting good at stuff. The harder you push yourself out of your comfort zone, the more your brain is growing. It's called **NEUROPLASTICITY**.

The bad news is that if you stop practising, the neural connections get weaker and eventually disappear. This is why you might find it tricky to remember long division after the summer holidays. You've lost a few connections while you've been den-building in the garden.

But let's end on some more good news (always end with the good news). It turns out that you can build your neural connections and grow your skills in **LOADS** of different ways. It isn't just about mastering long division or perfecting a double backflip in gymnastics. You can also build your **SOCIAL** neural connections too. Now, I don't mean that you've got some neurons that are a bit more friendly than others. I mean you can even get better at being social and meeting new people if you start to build those types of neural connections.

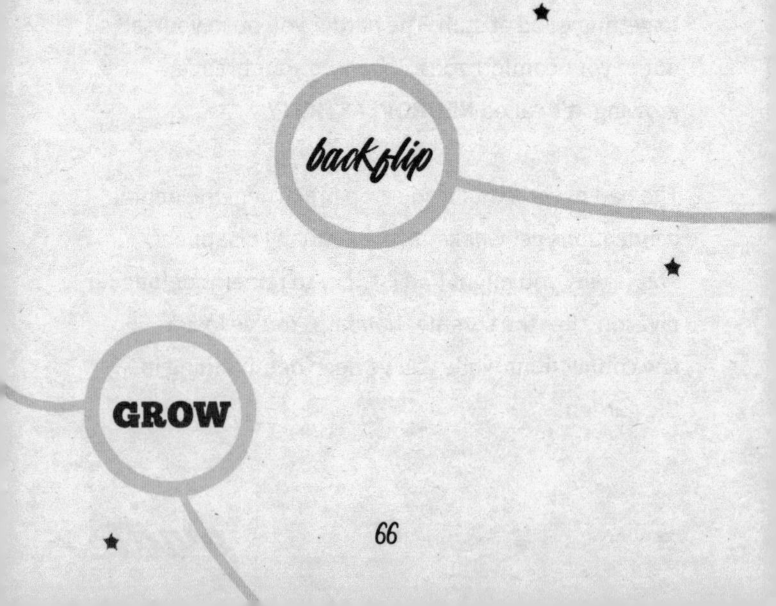

backflip

GROW

YOUR AMAZING BRAIN CAN KEEP GETTING STRONGER AND SMARTER

(67)

THIS IS IT.

We're there!

You've done the reading, you know that you can be **AWESOME** at (almost) anything you set your mind to. Now it's time to get out there and achieve those goals.

Did you know that research suggests that you are more than 42 per cent more likely to achieve your goals if you write them down? So grab a pen. No, actually, grab a permanent marker. And don't draw a shark on your arm (I did that once. It stayed there for 19 days) – instead do something sensible and write those dreams down somewhere. You don't have to show anyone. This is just for you. But writing your goals down makes you start to think about how you might achieve them. It helps you begin planning!

Now, we talked about the brain in the last chapter. About building new neural connections, and growing your brain and your skills. The key to getting really good at stuff is practice. And not just any practice – **EFFECTIVE** practice. There's a lot to work on, so we don't want to waste time on things that might seem like practice, but are not really building those neural connections.

Now, just before we start all of this hard work, we need to remember the basics. It's easy to get hung up on the idea that you need the best football boots or the coolest new pencil case if you're going to perform at your best. But the truth is much, much simpler.

If we can think about these four things first, our practice will be off to a super-charged start:

1 H_2O

Human bodies are 60 per cent water, so keeping ourselves hydrated is key to everything. Did you know that only 2 per cent dehydration is enough to affect your attention, memory and other cognitive (thinking) skills?

And if you're doing something physical and you get hot and sweaty, then you'll need to drink even more. Drinking water enables your blood to deliver oxygen efficiently to all your hard-working muscles!

2 PLENTY OF Zs

OK, you should definitely be thanking me for this one. The next time your parents tut-tut you for having a lie-in on the weekends, tell them that sleep is essential for your health and wellbeing. (This will also be great training if you have decided to go for the job of bed-warmer.)

Getting enough sleep improves our reaction times, speed and accuracy. It also makes us happier, less irritable, and more motivated. Adults need at least seven hours of sleep (hence why I take my lovely fluffy pillow with me on every single trip away – no kidding – I just don't get good Zs without it!),

but kids need a lot more
– if you're between the ages of 8 and 13, you should be
getting 9 to 12 hours of sleep each night.

(3) THE RIGHT FUEL

Does everyone keep nagging you to eat your greens?
If you want to get good at stuff, you should try to eat
well, because food is like fuel for your body. It really
matters at school – research has shown that kids
who eat more healthily do better, especially in maths
and reading. Carbohydrates, which you can find in
foods like pasta, bread and rice, give you the energy
you need to perform well both at school and in other
activities, while vegetables, dairy and meat or fish can
give you important vitamins and protein that help your
body grow and heal itself. So think twice before you
skip breakfast.

(4) SUPPORTERS

Now, I don't mean you need to develop a fan club.
You don't need to fill a stadium, or even your own

living room, with people cheering you on. But having people who can encourage you to keep pushing yourself towards your goal is **SO** important to success. Sometimes the support is simply practical – people to take you to and from training, help you to remember all your kit or to puzzle over difficult homework questions with you.

When I was 19, I qualified for the Under-20 US Open Table Tennis Championships. I was ecstatic – but there was one small issue. My parents couldn't afford my plane ticket. But, the most amazing thing happened. Loads of people from my street in Reading clubbed together to save enough money for the flight. But actually, they gave me more than just money, more than they will ever know – they showed me their belief in me. I am forever grateful. I went out there and gave it my best shot (literally, it was my smash kill). I won the whole tournament. I was so happy I almost missed the flight back.

So take a look around you and don't be afraid to ask other

people for help from time to time. It might seem daunting to ask a teacher or coach for help, but I promise you, they'll be keen. Or there may be people in your family who can help, or a best friend who knows just how to motivate you, or even a rival who pushes you to be your best.

So we've got the basics. We're going to take it one step at a time, with our support crew there to help us out if we need it. Now, we really need to get going. Stop talking about it and actually do it. And the final secret to getting good at stuff is that we have to remember to do the right kind of practice. Effective practice.

Remember Ellie Simmonds? One of the reasons she became a Paralympic gold medallist was that she trained against able-bodied swimmers when she was young. Training with people who started off better than she was. It wasn't easy, but she pushed herself as hard as she could – and it paid off.

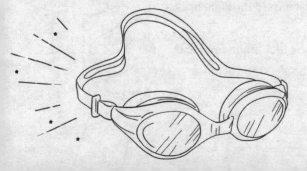

'I'M A NORMAL PERSON, JUST A LOT SMALLER. I GET ON WITH IT. YOU NEED TO GO OUT AND ACHIEVE WHATEVER YOU WANT TO.'

ELLIE SIMMONDS,
EPICALLY AWESOME FIVE-TIME GOLD MEDALLIST

So here is a short guide to effective, practical, purposeful practice (a.k.a. practice that grows your brain):

NOT GROWING
THOSE NEURAL CONNECTIONS

Football
Practising the shot I know I can do best

Netball
Practising with my four-year-old sister because I know I can beat her easily

Reading
Reading comics and nothing else!

Maths
Doing all of the questions I can already do

Baking a cake
Making the same old fairy cakes again

Making a presentation
Reading it to myself under my bed

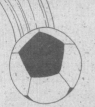

Reading

Reading a whole range of stuff to really expand my vocabulary!

Football

Practising other shots, from different angles, different distances to the target

Netball

Practising with my older sister who is much better than I am

GROWING THEM

Baking a cake

Trying out a rainbow layer cake with purple frosting

Making a presentation

Saying it out loud to the mirror, then to my mum, my teacher or my friend

Maths

Looking at the ones I got wrong last week, doing those again, making sure I can get them right next time

CONULSION

In the end, it is up to you. It is your decision how far you take your **AWESOME** journey. No one else can do it for you. You have to dig deep, be brave and take the first step.

There are lots of people who want you to succeed. Me for one. And there are people you can ask for help from if you need it. If you do **REALLY** go for it, you have **NO IDEA** how good you might get. At (almost) anything.

My story might be a bit like yours. I came from an ordinary street. In an ordinary town. I went to an ordinary school. I ate beef and onion crispy pancakes for dinner although I never did get to try the new bow-shaped pasta my mum was going to make the night we did The Network. I had big dreams, though. I dreamt of being the world's greatest table tennis player; being at the Olympic opening ceremony (as an actual contender); and I dreamt that, one day, somebody

(anybody, if I am honest) might read a book that
I'd written.

Dreams come in all sizes. They can be small. Like putting
your hand up in class to ask a question for the first time.
Or they can be big – like thinking about which job you'd
like to do or which countries you'd like to travel to.

Now here's the scary part … You might not achieve your
dreams. You might fail.

I failed at one of my goals. I wanted to become the
greatest table-tennis player the world has ever seen.
I didn't and I wasn't. Not by a very long way. But I
did get pretty good at table tennis and I travelled the
world playing a game that I love. I went to the opening
ceremony of the Olympic Games. Twice. And I know for
sure that my mum has read at least one of my books.

So, have I really **FAILED**?

Don't be afraid to fail. I chose (a long
time ago) not to be.

I chose to be brave. I chose to take every opportunity I possibly could. I chose the hard practice. I chose to learn from the mistakes (even the 40 straight losses in Japan). I chose to push hard to make myself better at what I was doing.

I CHOSE TO TRY.
EVERY.
SINGLE.
DAY.

What will you choose?

And I suspect I already know the answer to that, because ...

Discover more AWESOME

Paperback 978 1 5263 6115 8
E-book 978 1 5263 6133 2
Audio book 978 1 5263 6157 8

YOU ARE AWESOME

"I'm no good at sport ..." "I can't do maths ..." Sound familiar? If you believe you can't do something, chances are you won't try. But what if you really could get better at maths or sport? What if you could excel at anything you put your mind to? This inspiring guide empowers young readers to find the confidence to realise their potential with a positive growth mindset.

THE YOU ARE AWESOME JOURNAL

Find your way to awesome with this brilliant toolkit of goals, plans and challenges that gives kids the confidence to come up with their own plan of action. Whether setting out their goals, planning the best practice ever or keeping calm with breathing exercises, this is the perfect journal for anyone who dreams big – and who wants to make those dreams come true.

Paperback 978 1 5263 6166 0

books by Matthew Syed!

Paperback 978 1 5263 6237 7
E-book 978 1 5263 6238 4
Audio book 978 1 5263 6239 1

DARE TO BE YOU

What is right for someone else might not be right for you. But how can you find the confidence to be the person you truly want to be? In this exciting and hilarious new book, Matthew explores how to break free of the relentless pressure to be 'normal' and forge your own path to success and happiness.

READ ON FOR A
SNEAK PEEK
AT A BRAND
NEW BOOK FROM
WREN & ROOK

OUT NOW!

THIS BOOK WILL (HELP) COOL THE CLIMATE

50 WAYS TO CUT POLLUTION, SPEAK UP AND PROTECT OUR PLANET!

Paperback 978 1 5263 6241 4
E-book 978 1 5263 6242 1

KNOW YOUR PLANET

Knowledge is your number one weapon in the fight against climate change. Let's start by finding out what's so special about Earth's climate.

PLANET-O-METER

If you could choose to live anywhere in our solar system, you'd probably still pick Earth. While parts of our planet can get as toasty as 58°C or as ch-ch-chilly as -88°C , the average surface temperature is a comfortable 15°C. Compare this to Mars, with an average temperature of -63°C , and it's easy to see why we stay put!

Earth's temperature is 'just right' for living things, and not only because of our prime position in the solar system. After all, Earth and the Moon are roughly the same distance from the Sun, and yet from day to night the Moon's surface temperature swings between -173°C and 127°C. The secret to Earth's success is our atmosphere – the thin layer of air around the planet. This atmosphere is a mixture of different gases:

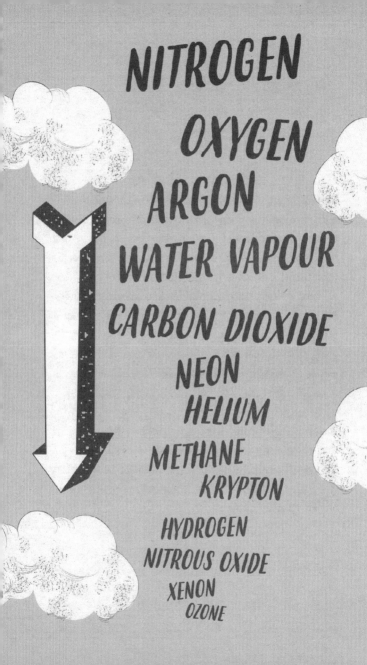

Some of these gases – especially water vapour, carbon dioxide, methane and nitrous oxide – are known as 'greenhouse' gases, because they trap some of the Sun's energy as heat. Step inside a greenhouse and you'll notice a **BIG** temperature difference between the air inside and outside. The glass walls and roof of a greenhouse are good at letting sunlight in, which warms up everything inside. But the glass is bad at letting this heat out again. The air inside the greenhouse becomes so warm that it creates a different climate – one where all sorts of plants thrive. Greenhouse gases work in a similar way on a much bigger scale, keeping the whole planet warmer than it would otherwise be.

The natural greenhouse effect is a good thing. It stops the energy that reaches Earth from escaping back into space (like it does on the Moon), making life on Earth possible. Without the greenhouse gases in our atmosphere, the average temperature on Earth would be around -18 to -23°C!

But a few decades ago, scientists noticed something worrying. The greenhouse effect is increasing, trapping more of the Sun's energy than normal. Around the world, each of the last three decades has been warmer than **ANY** other decade in the last 170 years. In central England, for example, the average temperature from 2008 to 2017 was around 1°C warmer than the average temperature between 1850 and 1900. A similar 1°C average rise has been measured around the world. These aren't just the findings of one or two scientists, but **THOUSANDS** of studies.

Earth's average surface temperature rose by 0.85°C between 1880 and 2012.

A 1°C temperature rise doesn't **SOUND** too bad, but it's not just Earth's average temperature that's changing. Earth's water and weather cycles are driven by the Sun's energy. Global warming has already changed patterns of local weather conditions. Northern Europe and parts of Asia and North America have become wetter since 1900, with less snow and heavier rainstorms. At the same time, parts of Africa, the Mediterranean and Asia have become drier. In the Arctic (where temperatures are rising faster than everywhere else), less sea ice has formed every winter since 1979. Glaciers around the world are shrinking as their ice melts more quickly than normal. The same is happening to the huge ice sheets that cover Greenland and Antarctica. All this melted ice has to go somewhere, and between 1901 and 2010, the average global sea level rose by 19 centimetres.

Armed with these facts, you'll be able to explain to anyone that there's no doubt that global warming and climate change have already happened. But will the temperature and the sea level keep rising? To answer that, you need to know what turbo-charged the greenhouse effect in the first place.

KNOW YOUR ENEMY

When scientists notice something as weird and as worrying as global warming, they work as detectives to find out what's going on. If we think about global warming as a crime scene, they've found human fingerprints all over it.

PLANET-O-METER

Don't look now, but there are dozens of satellites zooming overhead, observing Earth from space. These Earth Observation Systems aren't watching humans (so you can carry on picking your nose); they're packed with tools to measure Earth's temperature among other things. Collecting data about what Earth was like in the past is harder, but it's still possible. The thick ice covering Antarctica and Greenland has formed over millions of years, and is filled with tiny trapped bubbles of ancient air. By drilling ice cores (long cylinders of ice) out of these ice sheets, scientists can test the trapped bubbles to work out what the atmosphere was like long before humans were around to moan about the weather.

The oldest Antarctic ice cores are around 3 kilometres deep, and date back 800,000 years. Comparing today's air with the ancient air found in ice cores proves that the mixture of gases in Earth's atmosphere has changed. There is more carbon dioxide, methane and nitrous oxide in the atmosphere than at any time since humans appeared on the planet.

Where did these extra greenhouse gases come from? Well, we know that carbon dioxide, methane and nitrous oxide are released by all the things humans have done to make themselves at home. Since the Industrial Revolution began around 200 years ago, humans have been burning vast amounts of fossil fuels (such as coal and oil) to power transport, industry, heating and electricity. When we burn these fuels, we release the carbon trapped inside them as carbon dioxide gas. We've also released greenhouse gases by burning forests and replacing them with gigantic farms.

Between 1750 and 2011, human activities released around 2040 billion tonnes of extra carbon dioxide into the atmosphere.

The evidence tells us that **HUMANS** are almost certainly the culprits in climate change. By releasing extra greenhouse gases into the atmosphere, we have increased the planet's natural greenhouse effect, warming Earth up. And greenhouse gas emissions continue to rise. A record 37.1 billion tonnes of carbon dioxide were released into the atmosphere in 2018. That's more than 18 times the mass of all the animals on the planet (including all the humans).

If we do nothing, global warming, climate change and its effects are almost certain to get worse. Use the facts to explain that we've all helped to cause the problem – so we all share responsibility for tackling it.

Time to **GET SERIOUS**

WORLD
BOOK
DAY

SHARE
A STORY

Well **hello** there! We are

Overjoyed that you have **joined our celebration** of

Reading books and **sharing stories,** because we

Love bringing **books** to you.

Did you know, we are a **charity** dedicated to celebrating the

Brilliance of **reading for pleasure** for everyone, everywhere?

Our mission is to help you discover **brand new stories** and

Open your mind to exciting **new worlds** and **characters,** from

Kings and **queens** to **wizards** and **pirates** to **animals** and **adventurers** and so many more. We couldn't

Do it without all the amazing **authors** and **illustrators,** **booksellers** and **bookshops,** **publishers,** **schools** and **libraries** out there –

And most importantly, we couldn't do it all without . . .

YOU!

On your bookmarks, get set, READ!
Happy Reading. Happy World Book Day.

WORLD BOOK DAY

SHARE A STORY

From breakfast to bedtime, there's always time to discover and share stories together. You can . . .

1 TAKE A TRIP to your LOCAL BOOKSHOP

Brimming with brilliant books and helpful booksellers to share awesome reading recommendations, you can also enjoy booky events with your favourite authors and illustrators.

 FIND YOUR LOCAL BOOKSHOP: booksellers.org.uk/ bookshopsearch

2 JOIN your LOCAL LIBRARY

That wonderful place where the hugest selection of books you could ever want to read awaits – and you can borrow them for FREE! Plus expert advice and fantastic free family reading events.

FIND YOUR LOCAL LIBRARY: gov.uk/local-library-services/

3 CHECK OUT the WORLD BOOK DAY WEBSITE

Looking for reading tips, advice and inspiration? There is so much for you to discover at **worldbookday.com**, packed with fun activities, games, downloads, podcasts, videos, competitions and all the latest new books galore.

SPONSORED BY

NATIONAL BOOK tokens

Rob Biddulph

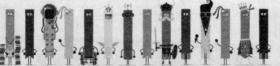

Celebrate stories. Love reading.

World Book Day is a registered charity funded by publishers and booksellers in the UK & Ireland.

Superfairies

Dancer the Wild Pony

by Janey Louise Jones
illustrated by Jennie Poh

First published in 2016 by Curious Fox, an imprint of
Capstone Global Library Limited, 264 Banbury Road,
Oxford, OX2 7DY – Registered company number:
6695582

www.curious-fox.com

ISBN 978 1 78202 345 6
19 18 17 16 15
10 9 8 7 6 5 4 3 2 1

A CIP catalogue for this book is available from the
British Library.

For my grandparents – Smudge and Dot x
– Jennie Poh

Printed and bound in China.